Do You Ever Wonder

What Happens in the Barnyard at Night?

To: Shannon ♡
Enjoy #2
hope you Wonder...
always Christina Taber
(2018)

Christina Taber

Illustrations by Amanda Wentz

This book is dedicated to my family and friends, for their unwavering support and belief in me. For my daughter Eliza who said "You be you mom." Those four little words set so many wheels in motion.

And, for all the amazing and wonderful animals I have ever had the pleasure of knowing and all those I have yet to meet!

Eliza, the little white mouse, is hiding on each page, can you find her?

Do you ever wonder...

What happens in the barnyard at night?

Do the horses dance
a quick step, OR...

Perhaps sing songs...

Do the cows and the chickens play ping pong?

Do the goats
practice karate?

While the farmer is sleeping, cozy in his bed...

Take bubble baths instead!

I often wonder while I'm lying in my bed, do the animals sleep? OR...

Author Christina (Ritty) Taber lives in Northern California with her family, dogs and horses. She has had a passion for animals all her life. This is her first book in the series of Do You Ever Wonder titles. Christina works alongside horses at 3H Horses Healing Hearts Inc®, a nonprofit horse rescue whose mission is to educate the community about the value, benefits, and life-changing gifts that horses can provide.

Illustrator Amanda Wentz lives on a ranch in northern California with her husband, horses, cattle and many other animals. She studied illustration and printmaking at California College of Arts and Crafts, and currently does illustration, design and western fine art. In addition to art, Amanda works as a professional horse trainer and riding instructor. Find her online at AWhorsemanship.com.

Made in the USA
Columbia, SC
30 April 2018